This book belongs to

....

Special thanks to Debs Summers for the support

For my two little stars and my Liz - CG

For my four-legged friends - SLW

First published in 2010 by Clickety Books
84 Carrick Business Centre, Commercial
Road, Penryn, TR10 8AR

Written by Craig Green

Illustrated by Sarah-Leigh Wills

Speech and Language Therapy advice
provided by Dr Sally Bates PhD, MRCSLT,
FHEA

CD narrated by Rik Mayall

www.clicketybooks.co.uk

Erica the Picky Chicken

Written by Craig Green
Illustrated by Sarah-Leigh Wills

Erica the picky chicken has
A ridiculously large bottom.
She has to have her knickers made
From super strength white cotton.

Picky chicken
picky chicken
Ick ick ick

Picky chicken
picky chicken
ICK ICK ICK

She thinks she is a groovy chick.
She wears bright purple lipstick.
Her chicken feathers oh so clean,
She loves to be hygienic.

Picky chicken
picky chicken
Ick ick ick

Picky chicken
picky chicken
ICK ICK ICK

When the rooster plays his tricks
She kicks him up the bum.
She can't stand silly antics,
She's a very strict old mum.

Picky chicken
picky chicken
Ick ick ick

Picky chicken
picky chicken
ICK ICK ICK

She's a nitpicking old chicken
Who sticks to all the rules.
She'll tick off the chicks for messing about
Like she's caught them nicking jewels.

Picky chicken
picky chicken
Ick ick ick

Picky chicken
picky chicken
ICK ICK ICK

'Til all is spic and span and slick,
She sweeps around like Frantic.
By dusting brick and mopping sick,
She wears away her broomstick.

Picky chicken
picky chicken
Ick ick ick

Picky chicken
picky chicken
ICK ICK ICK

She is a patriotic bird
Who fusses, flaps and rants.
The Union Jack is pictured proud
On her stretched elastic pants.

Picky chicken
picky chicken
ick ick ick

Picky chicken
picky chicken
ICK ICK ICK

Lickety split she'll chase the chicks
If she sees them playing cricket.
"No ball games in the yard!" she'll cry,
As she runs across the wicket.

Picky chicken
picky chicken
Ick ick ick

Picky chicken
picky chicken
ICK ICK ICK

She rules the farm, this picky hen,
This prickly old antique.
Clickety click, she makes it tick,
She's such a sticky beak!

Picky chicken
picky chicken
Ick ick ick

Picky chicken
picky chicken
ICK ICK ICK

How to make the most of your CD

On the page to the right you will notice a CD. On this CD, the story of Erica the Picky Chicken is read by the most fabulous and the most legendary Rik Mayall.

Depending on how you wish to use the recording, the CD is structured into the list below.

1. Introduction: Erica says hello!
2. Verse 1 and chorus
3. Verse 2 and chorus
4. Verse 3 and chorus
5. Verse 4 and chorus
6. Verse 5 and chorus
7. Verse 6 and chorus
8. Verse 7 and chorus
9. Verse 8 and chorus
10. Chorus repeated 3 times
11. Chorus repeated 3 times with the ICK ICK ICK missing
12. A shorter version of the story for younger children

How many ICKs can you spot when you listen and read?

Please visit www.clicketybooks.co.uk for more information on how best to use the CD.

CD produced by Matt Bernard and Jay Auborn at Deep Blue Sound. Music written and produced by Jay Auborn.